Stephanie Buick
Lucy Brighton
Oz Hardwick

Journeys:
a Space for Words

Indigo Dreams Publishing

First Edition:
First published in Great Britain in 2016 by:
Indigo Dreams Publishing
24 Forest Houses
Halwill
Beaworthy
EX21 5UU

www.indigodreams.co.uk

ISBN 978-1-910834-17-6

British Library Cataloguing in Publication Data. A CIP record for this book can be obtained from the British Library.

Designed and typeset in Palatino Linotype by Indigo Dreams. Cover design by Venita Oberholster

Printed and bound in Great Britain by 4Edge Ltd
www.4edge.co.uk

Papers used by Indigo Dreams are recyclable products made from wood grown in sustainable forests following the guidance of the Forest Stewardship Council.

Foreword

Storytelling is a part of the human drive to explore; to be curious about our surroundings and the people we meet. Whether through prose, poetry, song or dance, storytelling is as old as humanity itself. To lose oneself in an engaging narrative is to be transported to another time, another place, whether in tales of an ancient, mythical civilisation or inter-planetary science fiction fantasy.

Our lives present us with an infinite number of journeys, from the first faltering steps of a toddler to the fading shuffle towards the end of life. A journey could be a shift in dynamic between two people, a mood swing from tears to laughter, or that bright moment when confusion becomes clarity. The electrical impulses being fired as you're reading this are travelling along a myriad of neural pathways in your brain, lighting it up with images and ideas. So journeys and storytelling are integral parts of our lives and of the history of humanity. It felt intuitive, therefore, to merge these very natural human drives together in our anthology.

This theme, as we hoped it would, has attracted an eclectic mix of works, each of which, we feel, encapsulates different nuances of the idea of a journey. There are pieces dealing with universal themes such as love, loss, growing up and growing old. And there are other interpretations: the journey of a missing scalpel; a stormtrooper at a service station, and a galloping wine bottle. It was a truly enlightening experience to read the array of responses generated by this one simple idea, and we hope that you will agree that this anthology includes a rich and exciting range of both poetry and prose.

Stephanie Buick & Lucy Brighton

CONTENTS

Journeys:
a Space for Words

Moving Forward – Dave Gledhill

Walk a perfect path.
A thousand easy footsteps
when the shoes fit well.

Granma's Lemon Curd – Char March

She takes the sugar-nips and hammer,
hacks three handfuls from the solid cone.

I pour the Silver Spoon beet powder
till the scales say 225 grams.

She pushes her hands into straw and cluck,
pulls out three pullet eggs splatty with shit.

I open the fridge, the cardboard mouth,
cup two 4°C, Large, Class A, Happy, Free To Roam.

She has rested her head against the flank
as she pulled rhythmic hiss into the pail.

She has stood in the sycamore-shaded dairy
chugging the wooden churn, beaten

pale gold with ridged wooden hands,
pushed her hair back into her cap.

I prise open the olive reduced-fat spread,
tear back its silver top, weigh 55grams.

She asks Cook if she might have a lemon.
Cook unlocks the slatted fruit safe.

I take a lemon from the overfull bowl
of oranges, bananas, mangoes.

Then our hands zest and juice, teaspoon out
the stray pip. Crack and whisk eggs.

She is at the huge range, I the induction hob,
to melt the fat, dissolve in the sugar,

welcome the clean zing of lemon,
and stir and stir a slow watchfulness

as we ease the eggs in, and the yellow
begins to thicken.

The Inspector – Oz Hardwick

Down the aisle, a man with a sharp hat and sinkhole eyes
shuffles behind a black dog that sniffs without curiosity,
its streaked tongue lolling like a discredited flag.

This train has run so long, it has worn through rails,
through sleepers, and deep into earth, its windows smudged
with strata of abandoned life. We sit, side by side,

alone in headphones, dry eyes flicking at screens,
searching for signals, catching announcements too late
to snatch their meanings. Stations have no names, and doors

don't open. Food was promised hours ago, but there has been no sign
except the occasional smell of bacon or some other scorched flesh,
moistening lips but tightening bellies. Down the aisle,

the black dog glances up, accusing, while the man shuffles on,
drawing closer.

Flight to Finland – Bob Beagrie

The sun, out of the window of the plane, sets
my numb nerves atingle with fire as it sinks

into a sea of cloud 36500 feet above the Baltic
turning the vapour-scape into molten undulations

throbbing with barely contained eruption; a detail
from John Martin's *Sodom & Gomorrah*, the fire-eye

burning through empty space of the stratosphere,
my cheek blushing, my upheld fingers stained red;

yesterday a young girl walking past the foot
of the staircase in The Ship Inn, Saltburn, casually

announced, "There's a ghost at the top of them stair,"
and I resisted the urge to glance up at the apparition,

almost saying "Yes, and one at the bottom too,"
and one speaking, and writing now, and another reading

and the sun floating on the crust of cloud is already
eight minutes dead - an image of Lemminkainen

floundering into the turmoil of the black river
to be torn apart by all of the ferocity that lies

beneath the surface tension:

the political sharks, pike and piranha
the birthing cries, the weeping trees
the dancing ripples, the burning bridges
of clasped hands, monuments to unbridled
ambition, the bridges made from sweat
the houses of faith and their opposite
(which is also faith), the bridges fashioned
from sighs and shrugs, the rope bridges
full of shall-knots running over the heads
of crocs with their grins ready to strip
flesh and light from bone, take on
digest and transform the energy

and within this time of suspension in thinned air
as darkness comes on and the sun's searing glare

becomes a blood stain on the cloud-lake's sloughed skin
I close my eyes to ask, *what marvels shall we make of this?*

and wait for the pilot to announce the beginning
of our descent into the gravity of our worldly bodies.

Critical Paranoia – Ken Relf

Tim's got long legs and it's hard for him to sit comfortably on the bus, but he's come up with a way to lodge himself in between the seats with his knees wedged against the seat in front. He is locked in place and if the bus driver slams on the brakes he will be fine. This way he can read his book.

Reading is an exquisite pleasure for Tim, and on the bus he has 45 minutes to an hour to lose himself in that world. He wears noise-cancelling headphones to drown out the chatter from the other passengers – no music playing. Fortunately, he doesn't get travel sick so he is free to read, unharassed, until his stop.

Early mornings or after a long day at work, as Tim relaxes, he starts to go. The book is soothing, the words flow mellifluously through his mind and he begins to drift, as if he has become weightless. He feels his grip on the book loosen until it slips from his fingers in a riffle of pages.

He is reminded of Salvador Dali, who used to sit in a large throne with a big key in his hand. Below his hand was a large silver platter. As Dali began his reverie he would drop the key and it would clang onto the platter, waking him. Dali would grab his notebook and pen and sketch whatever he had seen.

The synapses in the mind can fire 50 times a second, with as many as 1,000 trillion synaptic receptors. The brain can create a world faster than the blink of an eye.

As the book falls.

Tim goes to other places. He floats to other worlds, fully formed in his mind, complete and complex and Tim is another person in that world, with other concerns and another life.

And the book continues to fall.

This time, though, Tim is in a car, in the passenger seat. He recognises the car instantly, the phone carrier suctioned to the windscreen, the wires running from the phone to the dashboard, the smell of drive-through coffee, the bags he can see in the backseat from the rear view mirror. He looks across at Linda, his wife, in the driving seat. She's on the motorway and an articulated lorry is in front of her. Tim sees it shift, the cab jerks to the left and the container slides to the right. Tim grabs the steering wheel and yanks it hard left as the container hits a car in the outer lane and pushes it into the central barrier where it folds in on itself. The sound of tyres screeching and thud of metal on metal fills the air. Everything not fixed down slides to the right, wires and bags and papers and coffee spilling as the force shifts from downward to sideways. Linda's car swerves onto the hard shoulder.

The book lands with a loud thump, the hard spine on the metal floor.

Every passenger jumps, as does Tim. Wrenched back into the present, the real, disoriented and out of place. He looks about him at the angry faces, and outside the window the rush hour traffic inches forward. His mind feels as sluggish as the cars moving outside. He leans down to pick up his book.

His phone begins to ring. His head clears instantly. He struggles with his pocket to free it and answers without looking.

"Honey, are you alright?"

Made of Mother – Gill Lambert

I've seen the photos of the drugs mules,
skinny girls in rancid cages, eyes wide
with western fear. Girls that packed
themselves, weren't carrying anything,
for anyone. I've read about the rape
of a girl in the Australian outback
and the couple dead on a beach
in a Thailand paradise. I watch 'Taken'
from behind my hands, knowing those girls
might be anyone's; might be mine.

I went from school to wife and mother
in as much time as it will take her
to save for this trip, go and come
back home. And I'm proud of her
for going, and sorry that I never have –
that I took a safer route to adulthood.

So I'm armed with a list of facts
that have no foundation in experience;
a catalogue of worst case scenarios,
gleaned from papers and the TV,
marshalled to change her mind.

And I tell her:
not to leave a drink,
be careful who she's friends with,
stay together,
don't sleep with anyone,

don't trust anyone,
don't take drugs.
Don't go.

But she'll leave anyway,
her things in a battered case that's been
from Blackpool to Ibiza, her hopes wrapped
in her Primark scarf with flowers on.
And I'll watch her go, my fears born
of media hype, my instincts made of mother.

Passing – Shaunna Harper

They've strung up your face
on canvas carved in glass
across the city's overpass.
Your eyes are bulging mole-hills.
Your hair is sprouting grass.

In the backdrop of a cheap shop's
parking lot, a broken sign
circles your head like a halo;
each fractured letter blinks
like gaps in a smoker's teeth.

Beneath us, the underpass is full,
littered with paper faces,
so I sprint up and down, stomping the ground,
just to hurt you a little bit more.
Your dirty skin is sun dust.
Your eyes, bullet holes.

In the spotlight of the city's rays
the wind consoles me with wary arms.
I won't make it home tonight.
I am a celebrity in my own right,
and you have denied me this longed-for life.

They've got every part of you
that only I once knew; your footprints are their signature,
they welcome you with overture.
Somewhere, during some innocent slip in time,

we forgot to turn the clock
and you ceased to be mine.

Now they've strung you up
like a WANTED sign.
I can't sleep at night for the deafening din
of your rough hands across my skin,
the cry of a speeding truck coming
like your sudden, throaty breath.

Every broken, burnt car
is a fallen, rusty star,
every flickering streetlight
a wish come true.
Your lips are silver instruments;
your tongue relays the tune.

And I remember, even in this cold,
how warm it was, loving you.

The Buck Stops Here – Andrea Tuckerman

The warning signs were clearly visible the second we turned on to the A-road – but he chose to ignore them.

He raced along in his Porsche, music blaring, headlights lifting and dipping like strobes.

"Jesus," he said, jamming his foot on the brake. "This really is the back of beyond, and you want to actually live up here? You are having a laugh."

I shifted further down in my seat clutching the safety belt. My limbs ached from hours of journeying deep into the heart of the Highlands in a flashy car. He wouldn't slow down. It wasn't in his nature. He was accustomed to bombing up and down the motorway, competing for first place. But the roads were different up here. 'Non-negotiable.' They twisted and turned like tangled balls of string, looping, dipping and twirling into unexpected knots which refused to come undone.

"I like it," I said softly. "It feels … mysterious."

"'Mysterious? What's mysterious about it? It's full of fucking rednecks. I mean just look at the way they drive. Jesus. Do they even bother to sit a test up here?"

He swerved dramatically, honking his horn at the driver in front as if to prove the point. I didn't answer, just glanced out of the window as we passed, glad of the darkness.

There were no street lights this far north. The night sky closed its eyelids firmly over the earth but the dreamy silver light cast by the twinkle of foreign stars somehow managed to filter through. It created a heavenly glow over the mountains which rose up protectively all round.

"I could die up here," I thought. "I could die this very moment, and it wouldn't be so bad."

I longed for him to stop, so I could step out into the stillness and dance, twirling round and round, embracing the Highland air. But he wouldn't allow it. We were making good time, and it would only embarrass him.

The car lurched to one side.

"Fucking deer," he said, grimacing. "Look at the bastards. They're everywhere. I can't understand why they just stand there, slap in the middle of the road staring at you. It's as if they've got a death wish, but they're too feart to end it themselves – they want someone else to do it for them. And I'm the man apparently. I'm the fucking man and I'm supposed to feel guilty about it. Pathetic."

He turned up the volume on the stereo and pressed even harder on the accelerator.

"It was their home first," I said.

"What's that?" he said sharply.

"Nothing," I said. "It doesn't matter."

I glanced at the high tech sat-nav. We still had at least another hour to go before we reached the cottage. I had offered to drive but, according to him, we'd never get there if I did.

The road opened out into a valley and the moon, which had been hidden behind a cloud, slowly revealed itself. It was a little brighter now but shadowy still, and I could sense the high peaks surrounding us. The effect was almost spiritual, causing something to spring open inside of me, something majestic and powerful – a match for any one of those mountains.

"Jason," I said, turning down the volume on the stereo. "I…"

A sudden screech of breaks and an animalistic wail echoed round the hills. Looking round I saw the tip of the deer's antler, bloodied and wet, just inches from my face.

I unbuckled my seatbelt, prised open the passenger door and allowed a rush of air to caress me.

The stag had been killed on impact, wrecking the car.

Jason sat very still, eyes wide open, staring into the road ahead. There was a gaping hole in his temple where the stag's antler had lodged.

A soft patter of hooves thudded to a stop by my side. Doe eyes blinked through the night.

I sensed the herd turn.

Taking up their invitation, I hitched up my skirt and danced.

Bella – Sophie Joelle

Ben came back from the school holidays the new girl.

Bella was taller than the other girls in her year. Her size eight feet, squished into size sevens, looked colossal against her friends' petite ballet pumps. Her voice had a tempting low jangle, threatening to break. Otherwise she was just like any other girl. Almost.

Some of the parents weren't happy with the "freak show" coming to town. They were worried the rest of the Year Eights would be confused by the sudden change and start asking questions.

"Well, why shouldn't they ask questions?" Bella's mum often argued with the other parents. "Surely that's not a bad thing?"

"We're just thinking of the reputation of the school," one of the parents said.

Most of the others were even less sensitive. "The main concern here is our children's safety."

"Bella's just like any other girl."

"She's not, though, is she?"

The bell rang, and Bella made her way to her first PE lesson of the year. Her mum had bought her a whole new PE kit, including a *skort*. It was a strange hybrid: tight lycra shorts hidden under a curtain of fabric masquerading as a skirt. Bella had protested at the school uniform shop, begged to be able to wear the baggy shorts she'd always been used to. But that was the uniform and, if Bella wanted to be Bella, she'd just have to fit into it. She had begrudgingly shoved it into her PE bag, a bright pink thing her dad had bought her. She hadn't had the heart to tell him that it was totally not her style.

Bella had shaved ready for the full leg display, but it didn't stop her from feeling out of place as she walked alone to the changing rooms. The corridors seemed ten times longer than they had done that morning, as if someone was playing a cruel joke on her to make time move slower. Her friends were on a different PE timetable, and Bella once again felt completely adrift from who she was and who she needed to be. She wished she could be jogging to the footy pitch with her friends. Instead, she was trekking to the indoor sports hall where they'd probably be playing netball. Bella had never been taught the game, and she bet no-one would want to help her.

The sideways glances and not-so-subtle nods and finger-points in her direction followed her like spotlights, making her stomach shrink to the size of a pea. She drifted into her own world where the "Is that Ben Havers?" "No, it can't be…" conversations weren't happening.

The PE teacher was already in the hall setting up, the rest of the class presumably getting ready. Bella looked at the two changing room doors.

She pulled her short ponytail tighter, wishing she'd pestered her mum to let her have extensions. The other girls had long hair that swished when they walked. They seemed to have swishy walks altogether. Bella was still working on hers.

Habit told her to go through the door with the boyish stick figure sign, but her longing to feel normal drew her towards the figure with the outlined dress.

But what about the whispers? The hiding-behind-towels? The curious glances and dirty-eyed stares?

"My daughter is a female. It's not her fault she was born differently," her mother had argued at the meeting with the Head.

"I'm just thinking of all the other girls in the school," the Head said.

"If Bella isn't going to be accepted here, then we'll look into other options."

The staff hadn't wanted that. They feared newspaper headlines and cries of transphobia damaging the reputation of the school.

So Bella was greeted back to school with P.C. smiles. But that wasn't acceptance, was it?

She touched on the handle leading to her usual changing room. Taking a breath, she entered the empty room alone. She sat on one of the benches and listened to the girlish chit-chat filtering from next door through the adjoining wall.

"*One day*," she thought to herself as she began to unfold the skort from her PE bag. "*One day I'll get there.*"

Up and at 'em – Lucy Brighton

Searching frantically in the 'keepsake' box for a recent photograph, I find none. They are all of her years ago. Before. I hold one tentatively in my hands. Nobody could identify her with this. She is laughing, the kind of laugh that only comes in youth, unfettered and abandoned. Her eyes are laughing, too. She must be about 18 and is arm in arm with Dad. Gently, I touch the picture with my thumb. I haven't seen this woman in a very long time.

Ring Ring.

"Fuck," I mutter to myself. That will be the home. Do I have the picture yet? Have I heard from her? I rifle in the box again. Nothing. I let the phone ring off. How can I tell them I don't have a picture of my own mother? They already think I am the devil in disguise at that place. Trying hard to remember when I last took a picture of her, I sit heavily on a kitchen chair. It must have been Christmas when we took her to the pub for lunch. Not that she would have noticed. Or remembered. The post-its, the memory cards, none of it really works anymore.

I can feel the nervous energy seep from me. I'm exhausted and tears sting in the corners of my eyes. It's not that I don't want to visit her. It's hard. She was always so vivacious. When I was young, I would sit and watch her curl her long auburn hair and apply a deep plum-coloured tint to her lips. "Up and at 'em," she would say as she glanced in the mirror admiringly. She always said that being a landlady meant never being seen without your lipstick. It is hard to reconcile the memories of growing up in the small flat above the pub with the woman who has escaped from the nursing home.

Ring Ring.

I can't keep ignoring it. "Hello...speaking. Yes. No...I know there must be some somewhere. I just...yes. I realise that...Ok. Of course. Thank you. I am sorry. Goodbye." I replace the receiver and exhale heavily. "Mum. Where are you?" I whisper almost inaudibly. She used to escape from the home a lot when we first put her there. "Early onset," they said. But back then she still knew things. Still knew who we were.

Knock Knock.

On the doorstep stand two uniformed police officers.

"Mrs Bloomsbury?" I nod and show them in.

They sit at the kitchen table and take out their notebooks. "The manager of the home, Mrs McGregor, mentioned that this isn't the first time your mum has taken herself off. Where did you find her the previous times?"

I pause and turn over the possibility in my mind but dismiss it almost immediately. "She would go to the pub she used to run when we were kids. But that's two bus rides away and there is no way she could remember her way there now. Not now she's..." I pause. "Not in her condition."

The officers nod in unison and I fight an inappropriate urge to laugh. They look like nodding dogs. "I think it still may be worth a try, Mrs Bloomsbury. Would you like to accompany us?" I agree and pick up my handbag.

As the car eases into the car park, I try to remember how long it has been since I was last here. Years. The last time mum went walkies. It hasn't really changed. It is like it is stuck in time, unable to move on. I briefly close my eyes as we near the door and I picture her young again, happy and smiling. With a heavy heart, I push open the door, sure she won't be there, and fighting the increasingly insistent feeling that something bad has happened to her.

The pub is quiet and it only takes me a few seconds to survey the room. Only two stools are occupied at the bar. Relief washes over me as I recognise the familiar figure of my mum. I call to her and she turns.

She smiles with lips neatly covered with a deep shade of plum.

Professor Baskerville's Pet Scalpel – Stephanie Buick

"Merry Christmas everybody!" says Professor Baskerville. His voice booms round the operating theatre. "Hysterectomy with bilateral salpingo-oophorectomy. *Splendid*."

His patient is anaesthetised and laid out on the trolley, a waiting feast for his ego. We surgical instruments, his cutlery. Maureen Collier, wife of Ray, mother of Mark and Glenda, and now, patient of Professor Baskerville, has been reduced to a face, squashed under a theatre cap, and a belly which heaves and ripples as the nurse swabs it vigorously with antiseptic.

He claps his hands twice in quick succession like a pantomime king summoning a servant and says, "Fetch hither my favourite scalpel, Nurse. Chop, chop." He wraps his meaty fingers around me, the dark hairs on the backs of his hands curled and sweaty against his translucent cream gloves. For a moment I see myself, slender and lethal, reflected in his gold-rimmed glasses, underneath the tiny reindeer flying across his theatre cap.

He begins to sing *We Wish you a Merry Christmas* but switches midway to *The Barber of Seville*. Dr Hamilton, his registrar, winces behind her mask. He pushes me point first into Mrs Collier's abdomen. Her warm, syrupy blood pools around me. It is like splitting open a pomegranate and I leave a trail of delicate crimson seeds behind me. He snaps his fingers and Dr Hamilton follows with the cauteriser, creating wisps of fleshy brown smoke, ruining my beautiful work.

We cleave again, deeper this time. He wiggles a thick, latex finger along the inside of the slit and says, "I love this bit!"

The pearly knobbles of subcutaneous fat spring apart eagerly as he resumes his singing.

We reach the abdominal cavity. Twisting this way and that, Professor Baskerville's hands, as always, lead the way in our dance, slicing and nicking, separating his patient from her reproductive organs.

"Fiiigaro!" he sings and slaps Mrs Collier's uterus into a large stainless steel kidney dish. "Figaro, Figaro, Figaro!" Droplets of blood spatter the dish and trickle down the sides, collecting around the crimson, mottled organ.

"Figaro, Fig..." He stops mid-Figaro.

"Is everything alright?" asks Dr Hamilton.

Professor Baskerville is staring at the clock. He slaps his forehead, muttering, "Oh God. The taxi. Paris. Helena. Damn. *Damn!*"

He drops me inside Mrs Collier and I land in a gnarled, yellowing canyon of fat.

"Finish up, would you, Doctor... Doctor... er ..." He marches towards the door, snapping his gloves off, without a backward glance at the startled faces surrounding his abandoned feast.

In the opening above me, Dr Hamilton's eyes, scared above her mask, come into view. She is holding scissors and a suture needle. As she snips and stitches with trembling hands, my bright hospital world recedes, darkens and finally closes and I am left alone with the sound of bubbling gasses, rushing blood and the bub-bub, bub-bub of Mrs Collier's heart.

I feel the jolt of the trolley, the flip of the plastic doors.

"I like your reindeer antlers," the nurse says to the porter, her voice thick and far away. I hear a faint giggle, a tinkle, and they begin to sing *Jingle Bells*. Inside Mrs Collier I wobble in time to the wheels bumbling along the corridor.

Some minutes later Dr Hamilton's voice is saying, "She's absolutely fine, Mr Collier. No problems at all. She'll be home in time for Christmas." Through sobs and snuffles, Ray says, "Thank you Doctor, I'm *so* grateful."

Now Mrs Collier is awake and whimpering, telling Ray that it hurts. He says, "Oh love, don't cry, you've done really well. You'll be home soon. Mark and Glenda are coming and we're going to have the best Christmas ever, a Christmas we'll never forget." He gives her a loud kiss, sending a tremor clattering down her body. It propels me forward and I slide to a stop alongside her internal iliac artery.

Once favourite, now forgotten, I lie inside Maureen Collier, wife of Ray, mother of Mark and Glenda, patient of Professor Baskerville.

I think of the highly acclaimed Professor, racing to Paris, to see his mistress. And with each quick pulse of his patient's warm blood vessel, I move a little closer.

His Shoes – Maggie Jackson

(for Aylan Kurdi, age 3 years)

It was his tiny shoes
that became iconic.

The footwear he danced in,
kicked footballs, learned
to tie his laces into knots.

His best shoes, perhaps, for a journey
to a new home, a place where he
could run and play in safety.

Such shoes should not be spoiled,
sodden, soaked in salt-water
that flooded his lungs.

Kick them off, Aylan, and feel
the warmth of heaven's shore, while
your death drowns this world in tears.

Meeting on a Train – Joanne Kemp

The girl's hair hung in a tangled veil across her face. Beneath it, her thumbs twitched across the phone's keypad with expert speed. Her boots were propped up on the seat opposite, Primark labels still clearly visible amidst the mess of chewing-gum and whatever else she'd trodden in on the way to the station. She'd annexed this corner of the compartment and it would be a brave soul who invaded her space. She needed no company and exuded the ill-fitting confidence of all the girls I'd seen grow up too quickly. Wrapped around her neck was a scarf – skulls dotted across its folds and, just visible above it, the tip of a tattoo unfurled an inky vine across her throat. As she turned, I caught sight of a gold cross and chain and wondered if she still put her trust in it. In her lap was a battered rucksack, equally tattooed with hearts and names – some blackened out, no longer in favour.

Text sent, she shoved the phone into the bag and scraped back her hair. I could see it then: the purple bruise blossoming across her cheek, turning blue beneath her eye. She raised her hand to it and, for a moment, the blank indifference faded and she winced before shaking her hair back over it. As we approached the station, she snatched up her bag, flinging the strap across her chest, and shoved her hand into her jeans to retrieve her ticket. No luck. She tried the opposite pocket, then back pockets. Next she started burrowing into the bag, pulling out make-up bag, keys, a filthy hoodie and a magazine but no ticket. I heard her exhale, curse in some foreign tongue, before banging her head against the back of the seat, eyes closed. Then, biting her bottom lip, she stared into the window, not seeing the platform sliding by as she tried to hide her face. She chewed what was left of her nails. At last she stood, shoved her way to the doors and punched the 'open' button. She slid out, slim hips sideways and elbows tucked.

She hit the platform running and I followed her but we soon came to a halt, rebuffed by a wall of commuters eager to swap crowds for the comfort of Starbuck's or an air-conditioned coffin in one of the tower blocks guarding the entrance to the station. I watched as she put her elbows to good use, trying to forge a path to the barriers. She got nowhere and faltered; a stationary pebble in the tide. Her phone was back out and pinned to her ear. She was gesturing while shouting in a thick east European accent, "You come now. I lost ticket. If I get caught – station police will check visa. If you want me to work, you come now with new ticket." There was a pause while we each held our ground against the press of bodies pushing us towards the exit barriers. Then she stared at the screen. "Hello? Hello! Can you hear me? … Shit!" She stuffed the phone back in her pocket. Whoever was on the end of the line wasn't listening or else didn't want to know. She twisted the chain around her neck, pulling the gold cross back and forth. I should have made my move then but something held me back.

Then her face changed, defiance surging back. She slung her bag round to her back, tucked her hair behind her ears and ran, shoving aside the last of the stragglers. She was skinny; probably living on Red Bull and fags, and snaked easily through, hurdling pull-along suitcases with practiced ease. Then she was at the barrier, hand on top, legs swinging together, up and over, landing cat-like on the other side. There were no backward glances in answer to the guard's shouts. Just one hand held high, the middle finger extended skywards. I watched, smiling as she merged with the crowd, her hair spilling out behind her, out into the sunlight. She'd made it.

Or so I thought.

Outside I saw she wasn't free. A thick-set bull of a man held her roughly by the arms and shoved her, head first into the back of a car.

Someone did want her to work.

Unspooling – Liz Flanagan

You leap up from wet concrete,
scarlet sucked away by invisible straws
as the car zooms backwards.
The open door seals itself, unslammed,
we eat angry words out of the air
my hand uncurls from your cheek:
its pinkness fades to white.
You swallow down that thing you hurled
the splinter of glass glides cleanly from my heart.

Your hair rises from your shoulders
you shrink before my eyes.
Lines erase themselves from my face
and you reach for me again.
Faster now, time unspooling, you unlearn to read,
you jump back, back, back, onto that bike
you wobble, then you crawl.
We grow closer, like we used to be:
I wear you first like a backpack
then over my heart
I carry you day and night
then finally we are one
I'm heavy with you again
our heartbeats tick and tock
to each other
In the silent hours of darkness.

Ice Cream and Raspberry – Liz Mistry

It was dusk when Jakey, sun slicked and clammy, wandered back from the burn. Damp socks thrust into pockets, laces tied together and battered trainers hung round his neck.

My dam-building medallion, he thought, proud that their carefully placed stones had raised the water to the bottom of his shorts. His friends had trailed off home, hungry for the cooked teas that awaited them, but he knew there would be no roast meat aroma in his house. He wasn't wrong. When he opened the door, the leccy was off again. Her cheap cloying scent choked him. There she was, in the living-room, face slathered in clarty makeup. Boobs bulged like melons from her T-shirt. Her skirt damn near right up to her ocksters.

Holding a brown paper bag in one hand and a handful of dross in the other, she clunked over. Ruffling his hair, she thrust both into his hands. "Got to make yourself scarce, Jakey. Ok?"

He scowled. She kissed him. "You're a good laddie, Jakey. Get yourself an ice cream from Giuseppe's later."

There was a knock at the back door. She plumped her breasts, checked her lippy in the mirror and hustled Jakey out the front. Before the door slammed behind him, he heard the thud of work boots on the scullery lino. Tight-jawed, Jakey shoved his mucky feet into the sodden trainers. Leaving the laces trailing, he mooched along the road.

In the darkening park, he sat on a swing and opened the paper bag. Inside was the jam piece she'd made for him. The bread was stale, but she'd slathered on loads of jam, so it was okay. Licking the last crumbs from his fingers, he stuck his tongue out and cleaned his sticky lips. He was still hungry, but it was too soon to go back. There was no food in the house anyway.

With the tip of his foot, he pushed himself back and forth. Eyes fixed on the concrete slabs, Jakey imagined he was still at the burn with his mates. Billy had brought a Battenberg cake and Ron had egg pieces to share. They'd got soaked and stripped off their shorts, laying them on nearby rocks to dry. The summer day had seemed perfect as they doggy paddled in the shallow reservoir.

Sighing heavily, he stood and headed to the café. Old Giuseppe pushed Jakey's favourite, ice cream with raspberry, across the counter. They both knew why Jakey was there. He didn't need all the whispering and dirty looks to work it out. Everyone knew what *his* Ma' did. Jakey knew who'd come in the back door. Billy Bloody McKinley. Big, slobbering, filthy lumberjack. Idiot thought he was a big man with his axe.

Jakey dallied. As the ice cream melted, he swirled it round till it looked like pink soup. He knew she'd be waiting for him now. Sitting on the couch, smoking, lipstick smudged, clothes crumpled and the house stinking of 'it'. He pushed his bowl aside, waved to Giuseppe and slouched home.

She wasn't on the couch. She was in the bedroom, a pair of tights round her neck, her swollen tongue lolling from her mouth. Jakey fell to his knees, tears trickling onto her distorted face. Finally, he wiped a grubby sleeve over his cheeks. Heart pounding, Jakey ran from the room. He knew what to do now.

Later, they took Jakey's clothes and gave him a T-shirt with Glasgow Celtic on it. It reeked of sweat, but it was ok. The police woman with the lemony smell told him that he'd go to a 'special house' for boys.

Jakey shrugged. "That's ok, the leccy's off at home anyway."

She ruffled his hair, just like his ma' did. "Because you told us where you'd put the axe, you can have a treat. What would you like, Jakey?"

Jakey smiled. That was easy. "I'll have ice cream with raspberry, please."

Endnote: For his last meal before execution, The Oklahoma Bomber requested ice cream.

Requiem – Hannah Stone

Her face as she entered
was tender as a bride's,
and, like a bride, she carried
flowers, the image
of their sweet history,
tied with white ribbon.

Tiny she stands
between these children
who've grown from her strength
and his whose shell rests here;
their vigour's muted
as they wait for instructions.

They gather all their love
to nourish her courage,
so she can take these few steps
towards the next boundary,
a separation
which she needs
to greet.

Stiff fingers unfold;
she places her bouquet
on the closed door
of the coffin lid,
a last embrace
before the procession.

Hypermnestra's Tale – Becky Cherriman

My sisters are always here,
trapped between sleep and waking.
On their aching shoulders
where once they carried
the heads of their husbands
are large bronze jugs – such a heavy load.

They pace the underworld,
barefoot and bleeding.
At the River Acheron
they stoop
to draw in guilt.
The vessel can never be filled.

Sometimes their tears trickle
down onto robes
that descend in waterfalls
around their ankles,
so close I can almost touch.
But can't.

The burden of a man's life is no lighter
than the mass of eternity.
Yet at least they are sisters in this.
And sometimes, when I lie,
trapped between a murdered father
and an impotent husband,

between sleep and waking,
I watch them pause to rub oil
into another's cracked palm
or race to reach the vessel first,
laughing at the hopelessness of it all.
And I am sorry.

One night I'll go to the woods;
I'll claw out a lump of clay
from the river bank,
carry it into my dreams
and to Tartarus.
I will plug the hole,

lead them out
of that dark place
and back to me.
For, Aphrodite,
there are other breeds
of love than eros.

The True and Genuine Account of Jack Sheppard's Journey unto Tyburn - Stephen Basdeo

Scarce does a week go by than a frefh inftance of infant depravity is fet before us. Jack Sheppard, a youth in age, but an old man in fin, was born in the Parifh of Stepney, about the year of Chrift 1702. He was apprenticed to Mr. Wood, a Carpenter, and might have cut a refpectable figure in the world, had he not, like fo many youths, formed acquaintances with abandoned companions, such as Elizabeth Lyons *alias* Edgeworth Befs, a proftitute, and Joseph Blake *alias* Bluefkin, and James Sykes *alias* Hell-and-Fury. Alas! – Now was laid the foundation of his ruin! At Befs' beckoning, he began ftaying out all night, againft the wishes of his Mafter, and began to difpute with his Mafter, faying his own way of working was better than his Mafter's, and defpite receiving many a found beating from Mafter Wood, Sheppard's heart had hardened, and his mind was foon difgusted with all forms of induftrious employment.

He foon left his Mafter's fervice and began cohabiting with his lascivious huffy Befs, and one day fhe faid to him, *Why don't you buy me pretty jewellery like you ufed to?* So Sheppard refolved to go robbing upon the King's Highway, and one day he met a potter and bade him, *Stand and Deliver!* The Potter replied, *I stand for no man*, and then Sheppard, unufed to having his demands unheeded, challenged the potter to a duel, whereupon he fhot the potter, and robbed him of his clothes and money, and left him naked in a ditch.

Another time Sheppard was walking through Hyde Park, and ftopped a gentleman of rank, whereupon he bade him to *Stand and Deliver*. He robbed the gentleman of two gold watches, and an expenfive pair of cufflinks, and the gentleman was so frightened out of his wits, that he became hysterical. Jack was apprehended for this crime soon after, and sentenced to death, on the evidence of the said gentleman, and was incarcerated in the Roundhouse at St. Giles, but Sheppard being a very ingenious fellow managed to escape, by climbing up the prison walls, and filing away at the iron bars.

Though any sensible Christian might have abandoned their wicked ways after such a close brush with the law, Sheppard continu'd in his depravity for several more months, and soon his name became the talk of the town, on account of his free and easy manner with Ladies of all rank; men and women trembled when they heard his name, but for very different reasons.

About this time he was approached by Jonathan Wild, the Thief Taker General, and also receiver of stolen goods, that he might enter into his employ, but Sheppard refused, and said, *I can get more money besides you*, at which Wild grew exceeding mad, because he controlled all thievery in the town, and vowed that he would hang Sheppard and his companion Blake at next sessions. Accordingly Wild, a wicked man, drew up a warrant for Sheppard's apprehension, and while Sheppard was indulging in drink in one of the low houses of Covent Garden, there he was taken by Wild's men, and put in the condemned hold of Newgate gaol. Soon after Bess was admitted to see him, and she exchang'd clothes with him, and remained in the condemned hold while Sheppard again escaped, sauntering past the drunken turnkeys, to the astonishment of all people in the town, which made Wild again exceeding mad, and more papers were drawn up for his arrest.

Sheppard continu'd in this licentious course of life for above twelve-month more, when, being worn out one evening from exertion upon the highway, he retired to a tavern in Seven

Dials, and upon becoming exceeding drunk, he was there apprehended by Wild and his men, and taken to Newgate, with manacles on every limb, ſo that he could not effect an eſcape, and on the ſixteenth day of November laſt he was taken to Tyburn in a cart, and his way was laid with well-wiſhers.

At the foot of Tyburn he ſhowed great reſolution, and acknowledged the juſtneſs and ſeverity of his ſentence, giving thanks to God, and accordingly the nooſe was plac'd around his neck, and he was launched into eternity, and afterwards buried in the Pariſh churchyard of St. Martin's-in-the-Fields. Thereafter his name furniſhes ſucceſſive generations of youth with an example of how, as Corinthians ſays, *Bad Company corrupts good Character.*

Before I Was Yours – Tracey Myers

Spangles, Fizz-Bombs and candy mouth explosions.
Collections of rubbers shaped like pineapples.
Ra-ra skirts and jelly shoes
that gave me blisters on my little toes.

Frankie said *Relax, don't do it*, but I did.
Deeley-boppers were all the rage.
I was theirs and they were mine,
sweet salad days.

Black trouser suit and crisp white shirt,
shoes polished. The silver badge
meant everyone knew my name,
but they didn't know me.
Cigarettes and alcohol, Britpop princess.
Good guys or dropouts? I'll dally with both
if I want. I'm ginger – but not spicy
and I don't end in 'teen'
anymore.

I'm a fully grown bird,
but my parents have flown the nest
and left me unable to fly.
Derailed and wild, I drifted a distance.
Got a grip, got on board another ship.
He told me he was *King of the World*
and he was.

White satin dress covered in pigeon shit:

A sign of good luck, they said.

Put one in, take one out. What you give
 is what you get. I gave and I got.
A surgeon's tattoo brought me you.
You gave birth to me on the day you were born.
Brand new, just like in the beginning,
before I was yours.

Return Ticket – John Harris

James sank into his seat with relief. Somehow he was always rushing to catch trains but had never actually missed one yet. When you are on the train, he thought, you can just surrender yourself to fate, trusting that you will arrive safely. The carriage was filling up. The seat opposite was still vacant but clearly reserved. James unzipped his case and took out a tube of mints, a copy of the Guardian, with the crossword started but not finished, and the book he had rather impulsively bought at the station. He looked again at the cover: *The Meaning of Life*. Somehow, right at that moment, today, Friday June the twenty-ninth, the title was appealing, with rather direct relevance.

James opened his paper and, concentrating on the cryptic crossword, was only vaguely aware that the seat opposite had been claimed by a middle-aged man of undistinguished appearance. A voice over the intercom announced the departure of the "eleven o'clock from King's Cross, calling at York, Durham, Newcastle and Edinburgh." He hardly noticed the clattering of points and the entry to and from tunnels, before the train gathered speed on its way north. Fourteen down was proving difficult. James paused and looked up, catching the eye of the passenger in the facing seat. A little disconcerting, a gaze more penetrating than he had anticipated. James recovered his poise and smiled in a welcoming way, inviting conversation. A vague smile in return, but nothing more.

The refreshment trolley arrived. James ordered a tea and cheese sandwiches. The catering staff member turned to the passenger in the seat opposite.

"Anything for you, sir?"

"Forgot to bring any money with me." The reply was matter of fact, without a trace of embarrassment.

"Do let me get you, err ... something," said James.

"Thanks, I'll have a coffee, some of those ham sandwiches, a packet of peanuts, a piece of that cake and one of those jam doughnuts."

"That'll be twelve pounds fifty all together, sir."
James paid, grumbling inwardly to himself about his generosity.

The man opposite paused from eating his sandwiches and pointed to James' book.

"The meaning of life; looks heavy reading."

"Yes, found myself looking back this morning; seemed to fit in with my mood."

There was a sympathetic smile before the reply: "It's the meaning of life in the past tense, then."

"I guess so." James paused, thinking about his life. Successes and failures, marriage and the divorce that had left him feeling alone. He felt the need to talk and his fellow passenger listened attentively as James described his life history, occasionally asking a question. The journey passed rapidly and James suddenly realised they were nearing York, his destination for the student reunion.

"It's my stop next. Thanks for listening; must have bored you."

"Not at all."

James felt an intense gaze.

"So, would you like to live your life again?"

"Who wouldn't?" said James, reaching for his case as the train drew into York station.

The man reached out his hand, grasping James' hand firmly.

"Well, good luck in your search for meaning."

Stepping onto the platform, James had a sudden sensation of energy and optimism. He had a strange feeling he had been dressed in a suit, but looking down he saw he was wearing his familiar student jeans and well-worn leather jacket. As the train drew out he turned to look back at the carriage he had travelled in. A face smiled at him from one of the window seats, with a hand raised in salute. He felt puzzled, wondering vaguely if they had met.

James looked at his favourite watch, a graduation present from his uncle. June the twenty ninth, well past the solstice. Was the best of the summer, maybe like his life, now over? Nine-forty five; if he rushed he could catch the eleven o'clock from King's Cross. He made it with ten minutes to spare and just had time for a flying visit to the bookshop. One book caught his eye: *The Meaning of Life*. A rushed payment and he dashed to the train and sank into his seat with relief.

A Road Called Duty – J. A. Whittles

Zhilan lay very still. She kept her eyes closed, not even desiring to peek through her elegant eyelashes. She didn't need to. She knew the purpose of each directed shuffle, each audible movement. But, today, there was a marked difference; an excitement that was being subdued like a python suffocating its prey.

Each morning, for almost eighteen years, Zhilan had listened as rosewater baths were drawn and her *Diyi* was laid out in readiness for the day ahead. Even in the summer heat, the hairs on her arms would raise against the coolness of satin which concealed her milky skin. Today, she would keep her eyes closed a moment more as once she looked upon this new day, her life would be mapped forever more. In the spring of her birth, no less than one thousand orchid trees had been planted in her honour by her father, the Emperor. In one month Zhilan would marry and, before sundown today, her betrothed would be announced to the world.

Lian Lu cleared her throat, bowing her head low. Zhilan stirred peeling the sheet back to rise. Quickly, Lian Lu placed her mistress's feet into her shoes. Only the highest *Matidi* would suffice today.

Of the potential suitors waiting, number four, a poet, stood in the hope of an enraptured audience. But Zhilan sat, unmoved. Her vacant gaze fixed upon the gilded door; she felt another fragment of her heart crack.

Before she realised it, her legs were carrying her across the room. She wrestled the *Diyi* from her body, leaving her clothed in only a white floor-length sheath. The guards moved to intervene, but none dared touch her.

"Let her go," commanded the Empress raising her hand. A faint smile caressed her husband's face as the memory of his own bride's reaction now echoed down the hallway.

Zhilan's lungs craved air almost as much as her heart desired the sky. She broke out into the gardens, welcoming the scent of jasmine. Free from her ceremonial robes, her stride never faltered as she crossed the bridge. She continued, youth on her side, and kept going along the road, passing horses and carts until she had reached the highest meadow in all *Chengdu*. Like bees, the poet's words thrummed around her head, still too close.

She glanced over her shoulder.

More sky.

More air.

Exhaustion eventually found Zhilan. She dropped to her knees close to a Khasi pine. *Enough*, she thought. Her relief was absolute. A familiar feeling then began to swirl in her stomach. It rose with an urgency like never before. Up through her chest, it grated against her throat. *How many times must I swallow this?*

As the scream burst forth, she slammed her fits into the dusty ground.

"I cannot."

Over and over the screams scratched her throat, eventually becoming weaker, subsiding into sobs. She tasted her salty tears. Lifting her hand to her chest, Zhilan lost herself in the rhythm of her heartbeat.

Nearby, a branch snapped. Startled, Zhilan looked up. An elderly man, with a long white wisp of a beard, tiny brown eyes and ragged grey clothes, knelt down at the side of her. He, too, then let out a huge cry, almost as loud as hers. Bemused, she watched this peculiar stranger sob into his sleeve until, after a while, he stopped and lifted his face to the warmth of the sun.

Silence sat between them.

Finally, he turned to her. "Good morning my dear." His voice was soft.

"Good morning," she replied.

"Sometimes all you need is a good scream and a weep to get through a day."

Unexpectedly, the old man then began to laugh. He beat his hands into the ground, creating little plumes of dust. Infected, Zhilan stifled a little laugh. It grew and grew until it consumed every part of her aching body.

"Or a good laugh. It works just as well," added the old man.

Echo of Eden – William A. D. Humphreys

This is the type of place
to walk slowly,
to breathe deeply,
and to shield my sleepy eyes
from the bright sun
which bathes me in a light
that I can't find
within myself.

I sit, watch the sea,
hear birds sing songs
about what could be,
and think of ways to start over
for the millionth time.
But every idea that comes to mind
seems too impulsive,
too unwise.

The sun beats down,
and I start to sweat out
years and years of
worries and doubts
that solidified inside my heart
and seem only to soften
when I pour whisky on them.
And though I know
I've long forgotten
how to fall in love,
I begin to remember
how it felt

A Spaceman Came Travelling – Rosalind York

The stormtrooper at the table near the door was drinking his tea, looking disconsolate. Some skinheads were living it large in the games area. I shook the road-fog out of my head and went up to the counter to order motorway tea and a muffin. The woman behind the counter slopped a teapot onto a tray and held out a tough hand for my ten pound note.

"Are you having a family fun day?" I asked, shovelling change into my purse.

"No." She picked up a dishcloth and wiped the counter with a manner that suggested she was *better than this*.

"What's with the stormtrooper, then?"

"Oh, him," she tutted across the room to where the white figure was pouring another cup, stirring the milk in with one of his fingers. "Comes here every day, thinks Jedis are real, and he's out to save the planet. I'd stay clear if I were you. Think he used to go to my church; can't be sure, though. They grow up fast, don't they? You don't know 'em anymore." She returned to slopping the dishcloth around, signalling that our interaction was over.

I went to a table near the stormtrooper's and sat down. He was trying to balance a teaspoon on his finger, but the white plastic of his glove was too slippery. On the table next to him was a pile of leaflets printed orange and turquoise. He didn't look in my direction, but said, "You're very lonely, aren't you?"

"Me?'

"Yes."

"No. Not particularly." I poured my tea as if there was a correct posture for tea-pouring for a twenty-four hour party person. I could feel his attention on me. Perhaps I should have listened to the grumpy tea lady.

"There's no shame in it,' he said. 'Everybody's lonely."

"I'm not sure they'd admit to it," I said.

"They should," he suggested.

I tried to look as if I had once known my way round The Hacienda *(Anthony, looking wicked!)*. I wasn't sure whether to be frightened of this white plastic weirdo or whether our ships would pass harmlessly in the night. Having my shadowed emotions hauled out of the dark like space junk seemed a bit premature, given the newness of our relationship. The stormtrooper stood up, picked up his leaflets and walked away with a clattering noise.

In the toilets as I sandwiched my hands in the Airblade, a leaflet stuck onto the wall tiles above it caught my gaze. *The Force is real,* it said, *and it loves you. The Force can save your life. All you have to do is ...* Oh boy, I thought. More self-help crap, this time wrapped in a celluloid fantasy. I don't need self-help. And I don't need lessons in life from someone who's gone off his meds and is worrying his mum silly.

I need to go home, churchless and Earth-bound, put my key in my door and go on ignoring the fact that the house lost its heart when I lost You. My nine-month prayer, burned up on entry to a hostile atmosphere.

I walked out of the service station. The skinheads were loudly noticeable. I skirted round them, invisible, knowing not to engage with trouble. The stormtrooper, though, had no such radar. The skinheads closed in on him. "What's this, then?" one of them asked.

I glimpsed a hefty hand take hold of a leaflet. Nothing to do with me. Surely there was a security guard here somewhere? Oh, bugger it. I turned towards the group and stopped short. The stormtrooper was handing out his leaflets briskly, and the skinheads were appearing to enjoy his enthusiasm.

Were they *listening* to him? One of them kept looking down at the leaflet in his hand, then back at the stormtrooper. As they walked back to their car, one of the others rested his hand on the back of his friend's neck. The stormtrooper lifted his gaze to me, and waved his crazy white hand. Something planetary caught at the back of my imagination as I waved back.

Insomnia – Kathleen Strafford

Arms tangling out of joint like foreign adjectives
clichés keep pointing their finger
                          look at this, this and this....
Jealous of my partner's easy breathing,
 I flatten my palm skimming his shaggy chest
when my cat sits straight up meowing inarticulate orders
as it clambers across my cheek
 I shield my face as
              personal nouns salute
at couplets, tercets and quatrains marching
 in military fashion   mid air

 disappearing and reappearing
                          in hooded cloaks

I stumble down the stairs following those soldiers

 warming up milk   a thousand syllables go swirling
                     in the cinnamon and white.
I grab my notebook under the day's clutter
where my new bottle of Merlot sounds
his horn   galloping
off my kitchen table   his red flowing over the field of
marble
                          and under the fridge

What was that?
Nothing dear...

The Wrong Coat – Martyn Bedford

As I sway out of the party, I unearth a coat from the heap on the banister post. It's the right colour and size so I pull it on.

If the coat fits, wear it.

Or is that caps? Yes, caps. Mum used to say that: "If the cap fits, wear it." By 'used to', I mean that she probably only said it the one time. I don't recall the context. There could have been any number of occasions on which she might have said those words to me.

I'm not altogether sure what it means: *If the cap fits, wear it*. The simple meaning is clear enough. But I don't trust simple meanings. If one of my daughters came across that saying and asked me what it meant, I can't guarantee I'd come up with an adequate definition. Not one that either of them would still be interested in by the time I'd finished.

Why am I thinking about my daughters?

Why am I thinking about my mother, dead these nineteen years?

Come to think of it, why am I thinking about caps when I never wear, have never worn, a cap. Except for my too-small, too-stiff, primary school cap with its blue fleur-de-lys crest that always made me think of feathers. A cap which I resented wearing but had to. And there's my mother again, yanking it down on my head with her fleshy knuckles.

There's a picture in an album, somewhere, of me and my best friend, David, posing in our school uniforms, on scooters, outside the front of my house, both wearing those caps. David's is at a rakish angle. Mine is plonked on straight, obviously too small, too tight.

So, if the cap *doesn't* fit, do you still wear it?

First day of juniors, Mum shouted at me from the top of the school steps, flapping a hand as if a wasp was bothering her. In the other, a cigarette. "Go *in*. Go on!"

"Is that your mummy?" a girl asked.

I told her, no, the woman was my auntie.

Do unto others as you would have them do unto you. That was another of her sayings.

It's not true that I never wear caps. On holidays, now that I'm balding, I use a baseball-style cap to protect my scalp from sunburn. I've owned a succession of them in recent years, each with an adjustable strap so they can be made to fit even when they don't. Each cap has been called 'Peaky'. Because of the peak. "Where's Peaky?" I'll ask, white-nosed with factor 50, stomping around a Greek (Spanish, Italian) villa, if I can't remember where I left it. "Girls? Either of you seen Peaky?"

They never met Mum. What they know of her has come from me, and from photos.

I can't say for sure she had a cigarette in her hand that morning, outside the school. She often did. So she might have done. She wouldn't have been wearing a hat, though. Her only hat, aside from ones she bought for weddings, was a straw fedora with a stripy band in the colours of her bowls club.

Enough with the caps and hats. Enough with my mother. This is about a coat.

Caps are not the point. The point is, the point *is* . . .

I pull on a coat as I leave the party. Right colour, right size. But it isn't mine. It fits, though. So I wear it. I wear it all the way home through the night-lit streets, let myself in the house and hang it (third attempt) on a hook by the door. It's a nice coat. Better than the one I wore to the party. I intend to keep it.

That doesn't make me a nice person, does it? Well, I know what Mum would say.

Indigo Dreams Publishing Ltd
24, Forest Houses
Cookworthy Moor
Halwill
Beaworthy
Devon
EX21 5UU
www.indigodreams.co.uk